Paper Republic LLC

7548 Ravenna Ave NE, Seattle, Washington 98115

Text copyright © 2008 by Mao Xiao

Illustration copyright © 2008 by Chunmiao Li & Yanhong Zhang

Original Simplified Chinese edition copyright © 2008 by Petrel Publishing House

English translation copyright © 2016 by China Educational Publications Import & Export Corporation Ltd.

Simplified Chinese-English edition copyright © 2016 by China Educational Publications Import & Export Corporation Ltd.

Publication Consultant: Roxanne Hsu Feldman

Published by Paper Republic LLC, by arrangement with Petrel Publishing House Co., Ltd.

Printed and bound in China.

ISBN 978-1-945-29514-0

The illustrations in this book were rendered in watercolor.

For more titles from Candied Plums and additional features, please visit www.candiedplums.com.

西西
CeeCee

by **Mao Xiao**

illustrated by **Chunmiao Li & Yanhong Zhang**

translated by **Helen Wang**

Candied Plums

好多人在踢毽子，只有西西一个人坐着。

hǎo duō rén zài tiào fáng zi　　zhǐ yǒu xī xī yí gè rén zuò zhe
好多人在跳房子，只有西西一个人坐着。

hǎo duō rén zài diū shā bāo　　zhǐ yǒu xī xī yí gè rén zuò zhe

好多人在丢沙包，只有西西一个人坐着。

hǎo duō rén zài dàng qiū qiān　　 zhǐ yǒu xī xī yí gè rén zuò zhe
好多人在荡秋千，只有西西一个人坐着。

hǎo duō rén zài wán fēi dié　　zhǐ yǒu xī xī yí gè rén zuò zhe
好 多 人 在 玩 飞 碟，只 有 西 西 一 个 人 坐 着。

hǎo duō rén zài kāi pèng pèng chuán　　zhǐ yǒu xī xī yí gè rén zuò zhe
好多人在开碰碰船，只有西西一个人坐着。

tā shòu shāng le ma
她受伤了吗？
zěn me lǎo zuò zhe bú dòng
怎么老坐着不动？

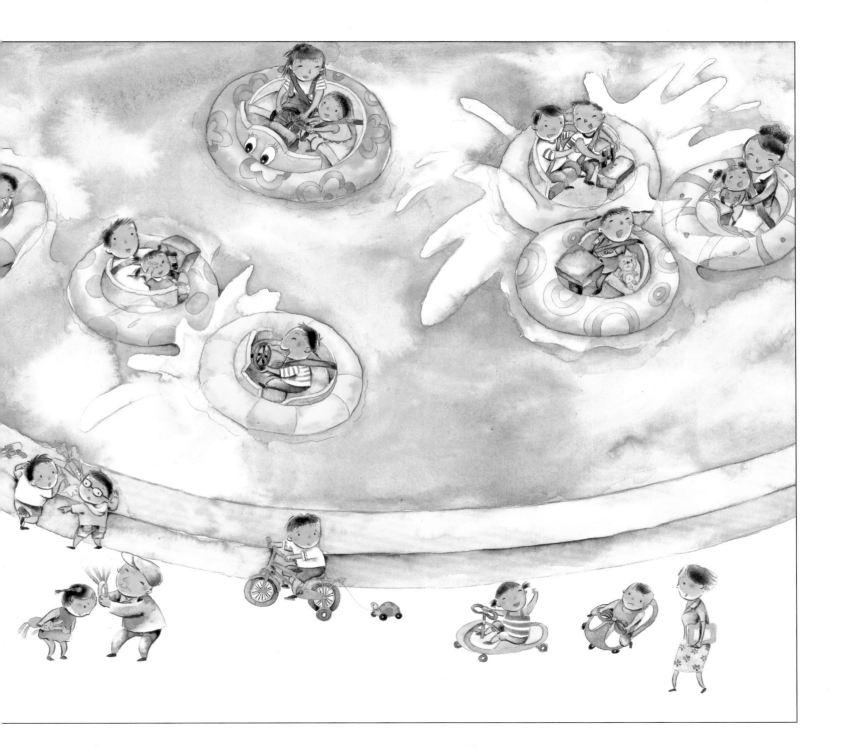

hǎo duō rén zài chàng gē　　zhǐ yǒu xī xī yí gè rén zuò zhe

好多人在唱歌，只有西西一个人坐着。

好多人在买东西，只有西西一个人坐着。

hǎo duō rén zài wán yóu xì　　　zhǐ yǒu xī xī yí gè rén zuò zhe
好多人在玩游戏，只有西西一个人坐着。

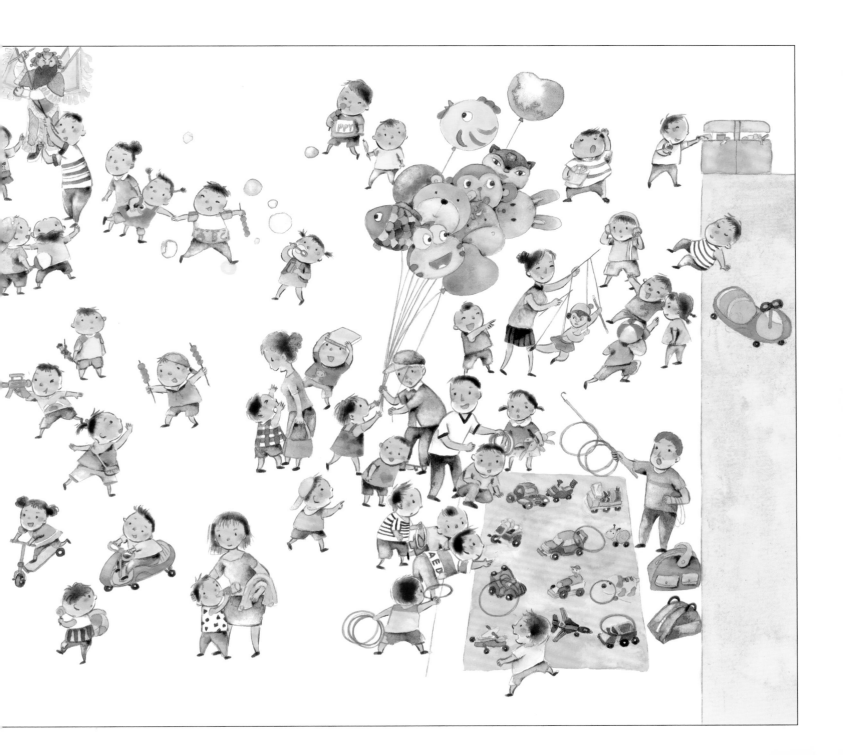

^{hǎo duō rén zài yě cān　　zhǐ yǒu xī xī yí gè rén zuò zhe}
好多人在野餐，只有西西一个人坐着。

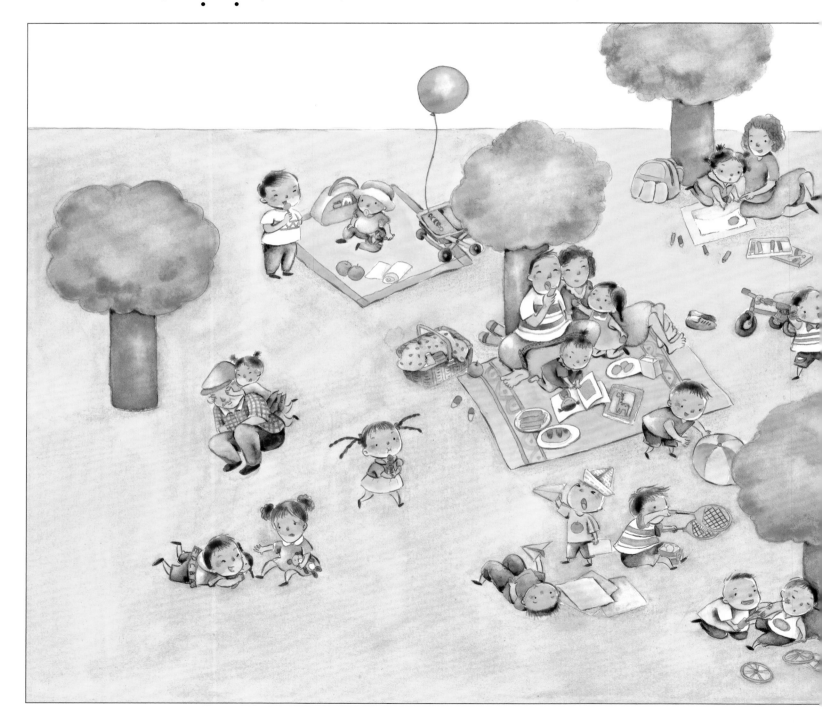

hǎo duō rén zài kàn rè nao　　zhǐ yǒu xī xī yí gè rén zuò zhe
好多人在看热闹，只有西西一个人坐着。

快来看，那边打起来了！

xiè xiè nǐ xī xī
谢谢你，西西。

^{nǐ shì zuì bàng de mó tèr}
^{zhè shì wǒ huà de zuì měi de huà}
"你是最棒的模特儿，这是我画的最美的画。"

This is CeeCee's best friend, Lily. Where has she been when CeeCee sits on the bench alone? Can you find her on each page?

Words and Expressions

踢毽子	tī jiàn zi	to play shuttlecock
跳房子	tiào fáng zi	to play hopscotch
丢沙包	diū shā bāo	to play beanbag tag
不舒服	bù shū fu	not feeling well
荡秋千	dàng qiū qiān	to play on the swings

不开心	bù kāi xīn	in a bad mood
玩飞碟	wán fēi dié	to spin flying saucer discs
开碰碰船	kāi pèng pèng chuán	to play bumper boats
受伤	shòu shāng	to get hurt
参加	cān jiā	to join
玩游戏	wán yóu xì	to play games
野餐	yě cān	to have a picnic
模特儿	mó tèr	model

For more language learning resources, please visit our website at www.candiedplums.com.

CeeCee

Many children are playing shuttlecock, but CeeCee sits all alone.

Many children are playing hopscotch, but CeeCee sits all alone.

"Why doesn't CeeCee come and play?"

Many children are playing beanbag tag, but CeeCee sits all alone.

"Is CeeCee feeling sick?"

Many children are on the swings, but CeeCee sits all alone.

"Is CeeCee in a bad mood?"

Many children are spinning flying saucer discs, but CeeCee sits all alone.

"What is she thinking about?"

Many children are in the bumper boats, but CeeCee sits all alone.

"Is she hurt? Why doesn't she move a bit?"

Many children are singing in the choir, but CeeCee sits all alone.

"Why doesn't she join the chorus and sing?"

Many children are buying food and drinks, but CeeCee sits all alone.

"Why doesn't CeeCee come to shop?"

"Perhaps she hasn't any money?"

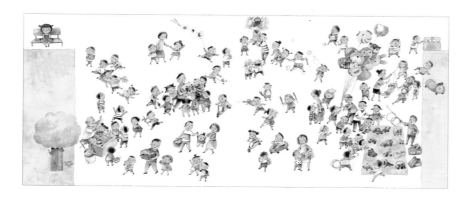

Many children are playing games, but CeeCee sits all alone.

"Was she separated from her parents?"

"Poor thing…"

Many children are having a picnic, but CeeCee sits all alone.

"Is CeeCee angry?"

"CeeCee, come and eat pizza; there's corn on the cob…"

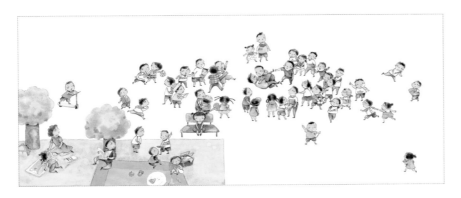

Many children are crowding around, but CeeCee sits all alone.

"Come quickly! They're fighting!"

"Thank you, CeeCee."

"You're the most wonderful model, and this is my best portrait yet."